Is My Child Autistic or Delayed?

CW00553154

By

Susan Louise Peterson

All rights reserved © 2013 by Susan Louise Peterson

No part of this book may be reproduced or transmitted in
any form or by any means, graphic, electronic, or
mechanical, including photocopying, recording, taping, or
by any information storage retrieval system, without the
written permission of the publisher.

Printed in the United States of America

CONTENTS

FOREWORD

In nine clear indexed chapters, Dr. Susan Peterson furthers the understanding and conversation for the assessment and in/accurate diagnosis of Autism Spectrum Disorder. *Is My Child Autistic or Delayed* will help families and professionals better understand autism-as scholarship, discourse, status, and/or spectrum condition. While Peterson intuits the myriad challenges of correctly identifying autism, she simultaneously unpacks the ways in which the general public, family member, professional, or naturally curious student of developmental disorders can improve their own awareness of autism and its associated conditions. We may not immediately cure autism, but this book will lead readers to better recognize and develop sensitivity to it.

Simply stated, everyone can benefit from reading this illuminating and forthright book. The two days likely needed to complete it, will return a lifetime of rewarding enrichment. *Is My Child Autistic or Delayed* should be required reading for those who are new to autism or those who think they know enough already. In either case, the book will share insight for anyone along the learning curve of this spectrum condition. It will definitely add value to preexisting literature and move the scholarly and practical awareness of autism forward. What I most appreciate are the evidence-based anecdotes leading to actionable outcomes that will serve families, professionals, and the general public for many generations to come.

William (Bill) Davis, Associate Professor/Coordinator-Photography &
Intermedia and Visual Art and Autism Workshop Leader Western Michigan
University, Frostic School of Art

PREFACE

$\mathcal{As}$ a school psychologist, I see the struggles of parents on a daily basis when the area of autism is discussed. Some parents cry when they receive the news, while other parents feel relief to know that this is the start to finding help and support. There are misconceptions about autism that make it confusing for both parents and professionals. There are cases of misinformation given by professionals to parents and then the parents are confused about the next step. The internet has even played a role in confusing parents when partial information is given with major assumptions about a child.

It is not an easy task to take autism information and the characteristics of the child to develop a personal approach to help the family in the acceptance step of autism. Once the concern of autism is accepted, then a plan is developed to guide the parents and the child through an educational process. It is nice every now and then to hear parents comment that they have seen major changes in their child with autism from the educational interventions and classroom instruction.

ACKNOWLEDGEMENTS

I am grateful to the many people who have influenced my educational and writing career. The many teachers, education professionals, school psychologists and students in the public school have presented writing ideas that never end. I certainly want to thank my twin daughters and husband for allowing me the time and freedom to express myself in written form.

In addition, I would like to thank William (Bill) Davis, Associate Professor of Photography & Visual Arts-Western Michigan University-Frostic School of Art for his encouragement and interest in understanding autism from an artistic angle. I would also like to thank Loren Martin, Professor of Graduate Psychology-Azusa Pacific University and Joanne Lara of Autism Movement Therapy for their comments about the book.

INTRODUCTION

The idea to write this book came one day as I (e.g. a school psychologist) was talking to a speech therapist in the clinic where I worked for years. We laughed as we had assessed so many children with possible autism concerns as the referral question that we started to speculate 'does every parent think his or her child is autistic?' Aren't some children just 'delayed or a little atypical?' After all, we all can think back when we attended elementary school and can remember other kids (e.g. or perhaps ourselves) that were just a little different or atypical. Some kids were a little dorky and awkward, but still grew up to go to college and have a career, while others had more difficulty adjusting to adult life. The word autism mentioned to parents can have a variety of responses. Some parents are shocked and in denial that anyone would suggest their child has autism. On the other hand, some parents may find a sense of relief and want to get the child immediate help and interventions for the child's communication and socialization issues. The purpose of this book is to explore whether a child is delayed, before professionals and parents jump to an immediate expectation, diagnosis or eligibility of autism.

Chapter 1
Autism Considerations

As a school psychologist working in an early childhood diagnostic clinic I am faced with questions from parents about the likelihood that their child has autism. Having conducted hundreds of multidisciplinary team assessments I found the answers to their questions about autism are not always easy. Of course, some cases are straightforward classic autism, where a child presents difficulties in the areas of communication, social interaction, repetitive (stereotyped) patterns and unusual sensory experiences. There are also cases where children present a few characteristics that seem delayed or atypical (e.g. unusual or strange in some ways) and this causes both parents and professionals to consider if the child has autism or is delayed in his or her communication, social or behavior patterns.

The professional and the parent both have roles in distinguishing the child's traits to see which characteristics fit in his or her pattern of behaviors. It should be noted that some children exhibit behaviors across the board in the three major areas of communication, social interactions and repetitive or stereotyped patterns of behavior, while other children show bits and pieces of a picture that is much more complex and where there may be other elements displayed that could fall in other diagnostic categories. We also have the information on autism coming from a variety of sources on the internet and in books. As a result, not all the information is accurate and sometimes parents and professionals make assumptions about autism on very limited information that may be biased or looked at from very confined aspects of a social or communication impairment.

The parents are often in a role of being given too much information and then having to sort out the information to distinguish what really applies to their child and what information should be discarded. Some parents can make sense of the information on their own, but for other parents it is confusing because they are told different things by different people and professionals. One professional tells a parent the child has autism, while another professional does not see any signs of autism in the child. Some professionals provide parents with very detailed information, while another professional may be making a determination with very limited information and knowledge about the child's communication and behavior. The parent then has to become savvier in interpreting what the professionals are saying and whether the information about the child signifies autism characteristics, delays, atypical behaviors or another totally different diagnostic or eligibility criteria.

TRAINING OF PROFESSIONALS

The professional conducting an assessment on the child may have training from a multitude of resources and institutions. Some of these professionals have medical training, while others come from an educational or school psychologist background. Often there are multidisciplinary assessments in early childhood clinics that involve many professionals who are determining a child's eligibility in autism. For example, some clinics may use a team of a special education teacher, a regular education teacher, a school nurse, a speech and language pathologist, an occupational therapist, a physical therapist, the parent and a school psychologist. As a result, different professionals are eyeing the child and observing if these characteristics are present in different situations where the child is working with different people. This gives a broader perspective of the child, rather than having one professional making a determination about the child.

Parents and professionals can get frustrated especially when some characteristics of autism are not clear cut. Parents may not be open at first to accepting the idea that their child has autism and it might take time for them to get used to it. On the other hand, the parents have a right to question concerns they have regarding the child's communication and social interaction and professionals must address their perspectives about those concerns in the assessment process. The ultimate goal is to help the child succeed in education and life to the best of his or her ability and skills. Sometimes professionals have made mistakes in this process. I once heard a speech therapist say that she has seen children diagnosed with autism in preschool, that were miraculously healed by second grade. Perhaps, what she was saying was that the child was misdiagnosed and never had autism in the first place.

It is commonly expressed that autism is a spectrum disorder and it does not present itself in the same way to all children. This creates problems for parents who may not want their high functioning child with autism to be in class with other children who lack many communication and social interaction skills. Parents must be involved with professionals to find the best placement for the child. Some children with autism are placed in full time specialized programs, while other children are placed in a half day autism class and half day regular education with monitoring by a special education teacher. There are some students who can function with very limited support in a full day regular education placement. Each child is unique and has very individual issues he or she may be working on in the classroom. It is important to remember that other children may have some of the same issues or totally different issues in the classroom setting. A program must be designed with individual goals that help each child with autism meet his or her needs in the educational setting.

DIRECT ASSESSMENTS

Direct assessments are difficult with children who have autism. Often, the child will turn away when an activity is placed in front of him or her. However, if the activity is left on the floor the child may pick it up on his or her own and complete the task later in the assessment. This is why parent report is necessary so parents who 'know the child' the best can comment on the child's abilities and skills. Sometimes this avoidance of direct assessment is related to the lack of social interaction and communication skills of the child. These children will often go to a corner, sit under a table or find a private area to complete a simple puzzle or block activity. In home observation, when the school psychologist and teacher are discussing concerns with the parents, the child will often disappear to his or her bedroom showing no interest in social contact.

Sometimes a disservice is done when one professional pushes for an autism diagnosis when the characteristics for autism are not abundant in the child. I talked with a parent one day who said a doctor suggested to her that her daughter had autism. It was years ago and she had no idea what the word autism meant. The doctor told her it was like the "Rainman' movie. The parent thought her daughter was not like the character in the movie. It turned out the parent never pursued the autism concern. Years later the parent confided in me that her daughter was fine. She turned out to have a common speech and language delay and didn't start speaking until she was six years old. The parent further explained that her daughter is still an introverted and very creative student who enjoys writing and making jewelry in her spare time. The daughter knows how to communicate when necessary, but simply prefers to be more introspective and quiet in her personality type.

WRONG REASONS

There can be many 'wrong' reasons a parent wants a child to have a diagnosis of autism. Let's take a look at a few of these 'wrong' reasons:

- A parent wants a brother or sister to have a diagnosis of autism so he or she will be in the same class as a sibling with autism.

- A parent wants the diagnosis of autism for reasons related to school placement. For example, the child can attend a full day specialized early childhood program if the child has autism rather than a half day early childhood program if the child just has developmental delays.

- A parent wants the child to have autism because they have a false sense that they will receive more financial benefits if the child has autism.

- A parent wants an autism diagnosis because he or she thinks more diagnoses are better. There have been cases where parents have shown up at clinics with a list of diagnoses that includes many things like cerebral palsy, autism, emotional issues, vision impairment, hearing impairment and the list goes on and on. Professionals must help the parent see what eligibility category best describes the child and stands out as a primary disability.

- A parent wants the child to have an autism eligibility to receive more social services and resources in the community. This parent has a false sense that he or she can only get support if the child is identified with autism. The parent must be given support when the eligibility is not what he or she anticipated it to be from the assessment. The professionals can help give parents information and direction no matter what the outcome of the assessment.

5

DECISIONS OF THE MULTIDISCIPLINARY TEAM

The multidisciplinary team usually has three decisions to make regarding an autism eligibility or developmental delays. First, the team can decide if the child meets the eligibility of special education in the category of autism or developmental delays. Second, the team can decide the child does not meet the criteria for autism or developmental delays as a disability. The third decision gets a little trickier. The team can decide the child shows some characteristics of autism (e.g. not an abundant amount of characteristics) and the team may wish to monitor and observe the child in a school setting to obtain additional information and data on the child. There can also be questions that the child's growth needs to be monitored for delays in the social emotional functioning area. This is because some of the characteristics of autism can be associated with some of the same behaviors related to other emotional conditions or delays.

Some teams may want to try interventions to target communication, social and behavioral concerns the child struggles with in the classroom. The team can then discuss if the child is making gains and meeting the goals developed by the school or organization. Further assessments may be needed after this time to see changes in the child's social and emotional functioning. Parents and professionals must recognize that some children need to be monitored and observed for longer periods of time to get a better indication of autism characteristics or delays present in the child. This book is written to explore many elements and aspects of understanding autism and delayed behaviors that impact children, parents and professionals.

Chapter 2
Communication Concerns

Many parents have communication concerns so there are often speech related issues when there is an assessment of the child. The parent will sometimes just say 'the child is not using any words.' However, the school psychologist and speech therapist are often looking at even more communication issues of the child in a broader perspective. Sometimes the child is avoiding communication all together by playing intensely with an electronic device, a telephone or computerized toy. The professionals at the clinic are really observing the child to notice the child's intent to communicate and express his or her wants and needs. The parent's information is important because of their vast knowledge of the child and home observations the parents have made of the child's communication patterns.

The clinic professionals are often helping to understand why the child is babbling or making vocalizations. The speech therapist and school psychologist are both exploring if the child's words don't make sense or if he she has difficulty describing feelings. The professionals are looking to see if the child repeats words in other contexts, if the child repeats the last words of professionals working with him or her, how the child repeats sounds and words and how the child uses gestures. How a child communicates is a big part of diagnosing and recognizing autism characteristics so there are many important considerations. Parents and guardians are an important source to see how the child communicates in a relaxed familiar setting.

THE BABBLING CHILD

Parent Concern

My child just babbles and makes a strange array of vocalizations — should I be concerned?

A School Psychologist's Perspective

Babbling is an interesting concept that some people have difficulty in distinguishing whether it is a characteristic of autism or just a typical stage in language development. The difference is really in whether the child is babbling as part of a process to develop language or just babbling for a repetitive effect. Another aspect is that of the age of the child. Young babies develop as they use the sounds to babble and respond to the language of others. However, after a child turns one or two and a half you may start hearing them use one or two word responses and later even short phrases. I can remember watching the language development of my twin daughters. One daughter babbled constantly as she was trying to express herself while the other twin said no words until she was confident and sure of herself as she used words.

The difference is when you see older children babble more for stimulation than language development and then you might want to look at autism. For example, autism is often more of a concern when the babbling is of a repetitive nature. One might ask a question such as 'is the child repeating sounds again and again just for the babbling effect?' The child could also be making sounds or even babbling vocalizations just for a type of self stimming that allows him or her to verbalize for a relaxation or calming effect.

WORDS DON'T MAKE SENSE

Parent Concern

My child says a bunch of words, but none of them seem to make any sense.

A School Psychologist's Perspective

When a child says words that do not make sense, a parent must consider whether he or she is playing with language or there is a more serious concern. If a child says words that don't make sense then a professional or parent may wonder if the child has faulty reasoning or other mental issues such as a loss of reality that signals different mental health issues. In autism, saying words that make no sense may be a lack of awareness to respond to social ques in the environment. It also can be an autism trait of reversing words. Sometimes a child will reverse the pronouns such as 'you' or 'I' or even using 'yes' or 'no' in reverse or respond 'yes' with every request. A parent will sometimes question the comprehension of a child who says words that make no sense.

Sometimes a child will say things that make no sense because he or she has a restricted type of interest. A child may answer every question with the word 'dinosaur' as he or she is overly focused on one thing and has limited play with concerns in pretending or using his or her imagination. At times, a child will say just one word like 'car' and the parents will say 'car' means everything and can refer to many things. The repetitive or ritual nature of some children with autism can cause a parent and professional to question many things when a child says words that don't make sense.

DIFFICULTY DESCRIBING FEELINGS

Parent Concern

My child just can't tell me or describe how she is feeling.

A School Psychologist's Perspective

Many children with language delays have limited words to describe how they are feeling. There are numerous young children who have language delays so there seems to be many children working on the same goal of building their vocabulary. Once these children build a stronger vocabulary they seem to be better able to express and describe their feelings. Sometimes a teacher or day care provider can help the child describe feelings with a variety of activities such as drawing a picture or describing a feeling through a puppet or dramatic activity. This is a process that takes time and some children made need more opportunities before they can describe their feelings.

Some children do have a very difficult time describing feelings about a situation and they may need some guidance and direction to help them sort out their emotions that are impacting their personal situations. The child with autism may not describe any feelings and the delayed child may not have the skills to describe his or her feelings. Professionals and parents must then observe the child in both home and preschool settings (if possible) or social situations to see if the child is able to learn how to describe his or her feelings. This is not always an easy task and the adults must take some extra time and effort to see if the child is making progress in communication information about feelings.

REPEATING SOUNDS OR WORDS

Parent Concern

My child just sits on the floor and repeats a bunch of sounds or words as he plays with toys.

A School Psychologist's Perspective

Sometimes the repetition of sounds or words is obvious and sometimes it is less noticeable in children. I think the key in observing a child's repetition of sound or words is the child's intent to communicate his or her wants and needs. Speech therapists often catch these the quickest in the assessment since it is in the speech and communication area. A child can communicate many things by repeating a sound. For example, grunting or growling repeated sounds may signal that the child has some communication frustration. Some children refuse to repeat sounds while other children make sounds, but don't repeat sounds when repeating is appropriate.

A child may be making high pitched sounds and repeating them for a feeling of self stimulation. This is different from a child making a motor or car sound to associate it with a car he or she is playing with on the floor. It should be noted that some children babble and use sounds or jargon with an emerging intent to communicate, while other children tend to use it toward a self stimulatory effect. Parents often make the immediate assumption that if a child repeats any sound or word that he or she must have autism. There can be a positive side of repeating a sound or word to show intent and then there can be concerns if the child repeats words or sounds as meaningless expression.

REPEATING WORDS IN OTHER CONTEXTS

Parent Concern

My child watches a television program and I notice she repeats the lines of the program often throughout the day.

A School Psychologist's Perspective

Repeating words in other contexts is often noticed as an autism characteristic. Sometimes a teacher or parent will ask the child a question and instead of answering it the child will simply repeat the question. Sometimes a child is observed repeating words in other contexts as the child repeats a television program song or line hours after the program was turned off. A cute catchy phrase from a commercial or television show may be repeated by children in the house as a fun response. However, a child with autism concerns may be saying this without meaning.

At times, parent don't catch that when a child uses a social greeting he or she may be using it as a repetitive phrase that has been heard before in a different setting. For example, the child answers the door and says, "hi, how are you?" not as a social greeting, but really as a repetitive phrase. At first, a parent may think that the child communicates well and has good social skills, but upon further observation one can see that the child really does not understand what the words mean. I think it is important to realize that a typical developing child may repeat or sing words of a favorite song from a television program he or she enjoys. Repeating words out of context must be viewed in a practical sense of how the child is using language.

REPEATING THE LAST WORD OR PHRASE

Parent Concern

My child just repeats the last words I speak. If I say the words 'look here,' my child just repeats the words and doesn't even look toward me.

A School Psychologist's Perspective

Sometimes children repeat the last word spoken from another individual. If the teacher says 'point to the dog' the child may repeat 'point to the dog' instead of following the request. Rote phrases such as 'see book' or 'say the ABC's' are used, but meaning associated with phrases is not always present. These repetitive phrases can also be inconsistent as the child simply repeats 'yes or no' rather than responding correctly to a question or comment. Parents often get frustrated by this because they don't understand how to help the child meet his or her needs.

If the school psychologist says 'we will go to nurse' the child may repeat 'go to nurse' numerous times as they walk down the hall. I worked with a teacher from England and some children had an excellent ear for repeating sing song pitches and at times would pronounce and repeat words with the English accent or mimic the inflection patterns of the teacher. The professionals are often looking to see if the child has an understanding of the meaning of the words and phrases he or she is speaking. They want to see if the words are being used to communicate a thought or idea, rather than just repetition of words with no meaning or limited meaning.

USING GESTURES

My child grabs an object and pulls it from my hand when he wants something. He is not even looking at me and seems to be looking at the floor or ceiling.

A School Psychologist's Perspective

A common autistic characteristic is using gestures instead of words to get or acquire the items that he or she wants to have. However, these nonverbal gestures are not always appropriate. A child may grab an object and pull it from the school psychologist or teacher, while focusing his or her eyes on the ceiling, the floor or another part of the room and make limited eye contact and social exchange. Children with autism characteristics may have inconsistent pointing responses. The teacher points to something and the child looks at the person's pointed finger rather than at the object.

Another way young children with autism communicate is by pulling someone or someone's hand to a desired object. Young children may be showing signs of progress if they actually take an object, approach a person and hand the person the object as an indication that the child needs assistance or wants help with something. Hand signals are used as a way to answer questions. When asked his or her age, the child may hold up three fingers rather than verbally answer 'three.' Again the professional and parent must examine if the child is making an effort to communicate by using the gestures in social interaction.

STRONG INTEREST IN ELECTRONIC DEVICES

Parent Concern

My child is like a genesis. She plays electronic games and can match shapes and play memory games.

A School Psychologist's Perspective

As a school psychologist I have seen numerous children with fantastic technological skills. The student can play games and often knows every color, sometimes many letters and numbers and would probably score well on an academic readiness test. However, when language is requested in tasks the child with autism has a difficult time. The child may not be able to ask for a drink of water or request going to the bathroom. When a teacher asks the child, 'which animal is big?' the child cannot respond to a language based question even though he just had to point to the big animal in the picture.

Electronic devices often take away the need to communicate. The child with autism and or speech delays has a difficult time with language, communication and the social parts of language. I notice that parents often brag at the wonderful skills the child has in playing games on the computer. In assessments, I have seen children tantrum to use the parent's phone to play technological games. Parents have concerns about speech delays, but don't always see that an electronic device is taking away opportunities to have social interaction. All of these actions, allow the child to go into his or her own personal technological world and avoid the communication and socialization with peers and adults.

Chapter 3
Stereotyped Behavior Concerns

Stereotyped behavior concerns are not always noticed by parents as they just get used to the child doing something in a particular way. Sometimes the parents just consider that this is the child's habit and the parents really don't see these stereotyped behavior concerns as issues. The school psychologist sometimes needs to point out that a child is head banging or staring blankly at objects. The parent may not notice the repetitious movements, the quick darting movements or the repetitive tasks of the child. Professionals are often pointing out to the parents the lining up rituals of the child during the assessment. Parents may not notice the extent the child is lining up the toys or objects and how precise the order of the objects has to be for the child. It is really helpful if the professional and the parents work together to get a full picture of the child's repetitive behaviors.

Another area the parents may mention is that activities and requests for the child should always be presented in the same way. Parents will sometimes want questions to be asked in a certain way. For example, they want the professional to say 'touch the blue color' instead of 'point to the blue color.' At other times, the parent wants the school psychologist to demonstrate how to do an activity in a precise way that the child is used to in the home setting. The key area the school psychologist is trying to see is if the child is flexible in being approached with a task presented in a different way.

TASKS-COMPLETED IN A CERTAIN WAY

Parent Concern

My child knows how to do that activity, but he doesn't know you so he won't do it for you. If you ask him to do it in a certain way or by his in-home developmental specialist, then he can do it.

A School Psychologist's Perspective

Your child should be able to show his or her abilities and skills with a variety of people in many settings. A child should be able to show his skill or ability to complete a task without a specific prompt always being given or only by a specific person. Professionals are looking for the child's consistency in completing the request or task. A professional is really asking 'does the child have the skill to complete the task?' I think the professional is trying to help the parent see that life is not set up in a perfectly controlled setting with ques, signals and prompts given before every request.

Many professionals want the child to be able to transfer the skills he or she learns to a variety of settings whether the child has autism or developmental delays. This can be as simple as learning to clean up a play area or pick up toys without singing a certain song every time a request is made. Yes, it is fun for the teacher to sing the clean up song, but there may be another time when she has a sore throat and whispers to the children to clean up the play area. The child is learning the ability to adapt his or her learning skills to a variety of settings in a widespread practical world.

HEAD BANGING

Parent Concern

My child bangs his head, but I think he is just trying to express his own frustrations.

A School Psychologist's Perspective

Head banging can occur for a variety of reasons. A child may be head banging because he or she has not developed enough language to express his or her own needs. The child may not have the vocabulary and does not know how to ask for a drink of juice so he or she does whatever will make some noise and get some attention. A child may bang his or her head on the crib to gain attention and get noticed. The young child may head bang as he or she is trying to gain attention to make a request for a diaper change. Once the request is noticed the child may stop banging his or her head until another need occurs.

At other times, a child may bang his or her head to indicate "I'm sick" from a headache or ear infection. There was one child who his parents described as a head banger, but upon closer examination by the physical therapist it was noted that boy actually had poor balance control and was uncoordinated as the reason he would bang his head and throw himself to the floor. Head banging could be related to autism as a self injury type of behavior or lack of response to pain. In one assessment, the speech therapist noticed the child kept crawling under the desk and banging his head on the side of the desk for stimulation. It could also be a habit disorder where the child bangs his head for something to do when he or she is bored.

BLANK STARES

Parent Concern

My child stares blankly at objects so I think she has autism.

A School Psychologist's Perspective

Blank stares can be seen in children under different contexts. For example, a child with epilepsy or what is called a seizure disorder may have short periods of time where he or she stares blankly or has a short seizure. A child who is sick may lay quietly and stare blankly in a room. Sometimes staring at an object could be appropriate as a child may be showing a curiosity or interest in understanding how a toy moves or an object works.

My observation of children with autism is that they tend to stare longer at objects. For example, in one elementary school where I worked the teacher commented how some of the children with autism on the playground would stare for extended periods of time at a small rock or stone on the ground near the playground equipment. Sometimes students with autism would run away from the teacher or even attempt to leave the school ground and run down the street. The school staff would look everywhere for the child and then they would often find the child staring blankly at an object in the environment. One child was found as he was watching a street sign rotate back and forth from a gentle breeze. Another child was found as he was watching a tree branch blowing in the wind. Sometimes a child with autism stares to see the motion of a ceiling fan rotating over and over again.

REPETITIOUS MOVEMENTS

Parent Concern

My daughter rocks back and forth when she plays with blocks on the floor.

A School Psychologist's Perspective

Repetitious movements are often pointed out as a concern in autism assessments. As a former teacher of three and four year olds for many years (e.g. before becoming a school psychologist), I am cautious when I question parents about a child's movement patterns. I often feel a need to explain to parents the concern of continuous repetitious movements in the child. Repetitious movements can refer to several areas. One area often discussed is does the child rock him or herself in a back and forth position for lengthy periods of time which could be while seated or standing up. Part of this is simply observation of the child and sometimes parents are aware of these repetitious movements and at other times they don't notice the movements at all.

As the assessment process is being conducted the child is being observed to see if he or she is sitting still or continuing rocking back and forth. The school psychologist may look over in the assessment and point out if the child is sitting quietly building with the blocks or turning around constantly. Other repetitious movements can include flicking fingers, hand flapping or toe walking. Some repetitious movements are obvious to the parent and school psychologist and some movements need to be observed to see if they are in abundance or only an occasional occurrence.

QUICK DARTING MOVEMENTS

Parent Concern

My son just makes quick movements all over the house and its driving me crazy.

A School Psychologist's Perspective

Another area looked at is if the child darts around the room and moves quickly in the room or hallway. Many parents of young children would answer a question of this type of movement with a big 'yes.' I think that parents sometimes misinterpret this question. They are associating that a child can out run them down the hall so of course the child is a fast runner. However, I think the school psychologist is often looking more at patterns of behavior. Is this child quickly darting from one activity to another without paying any attention to what he or she is doing? Is this the child who darts around the room quickly taking all the toys off of the shelf, but not really playing with any of the toys for an extended period of time? Is the child darting around the room in a way that is almost pacing back and forth as he or she has developed a path to be completed quickly and repetitively in the house?

This is where observation plays a key in understanding the child's behavior. Sometimes a school psychologist will want to observe how a child darts around in a small office or a long hallway where mom is chasing him or her around a large open space. I notice when a child has a tendency to dart quickly the parent immediately closes the door when entering the office. At other times a school psychologist may make a home visit to see how the child darts and moves in a familiar home environment versus an unfamiliar environment such as an office or classroom.

REPETITIVE TASKS

Parent Concern

My child just reads the same book over and over again.

A School Psychologist's Perspective

Repetitive tasks can be both appropriate and inappropriate as one examines a child's behavior. I once heard of an autism referral once from a preschool and the only repetitive task or behavior the child had was that he 'read the same book over and over again.' This referral would have immediately sent up red flags to me. After all it is not uncommon for a child to frequently request the same book again and again. It is showing their love for learning and reading books. Sometimes a child may be filling in parts of a story or working on memorizing a part or passage in the book. It could have been that the child was learning through repetition. If the young boy came to that evaluation and was socially interactive, communicated well, followed directions and was just a curious little boy who loved books then repetitive tasks would be a positive task for him.

Repetitive tasks with no particular purpose seem to stand out when assessing autism characteristics. A child who turns the lights on and off, opens and closes the door and even paces back and forth across the room signals repetitive tasks being done without a direct purpose. Again, a child watching the same movie or television show over and over again may be having a similar experience as the child reading the book over numerous times. After all, there are many adults that love to watch the same movies over again. The question becomes is the repetitive task showing an intent to do something or without a real purpose.

LINING-UP RITUALS

Parent Concern

My child lines up cars so I think he is autistic.

A School Psychologist's Perspective

Lining up objects is one of the most common reasons parents seem to mention for an autism assessment. The concept of lining up objects needs to be explored for both typical lining up and the ritualistic lining up of objects. For example, lining up a toy train would be fairly typical as trains go in a lined up fashion. Also baby duck toys lined up to follow the mother duck would seem to be a typical play pattern. It should be noted that some children who line up or organize toys get higher marks in their cognitive abilities because of their ability to sort by colors, shapes and forms.

Where lining up objects becomes almost ritualistic is when the behavior becomes more noticeable. For example, some professionals indicate it is in the intensity in how the child lines up objects. Lining up cars may be appropriate for many children, but for some other children they may become very disturbed if even one car is not evenly matched bumper to bumper or if someone touches all or any of the red cars. Some children may line up cars across the entire house and if anyone disturbs any part of the lined up cars there is a major tantrum. Children with autism have been known to line up other items than toys such as computer discs, hair clips, books and different types of foods.

PLACE OBJECTS IN A CERTAIN ORDER

Parent Concern

My child takes all of her clothes out of the closet and off of the hangers to be placed on the floor, is this typical?

A School Psychologist's Perspective

This is one of the repetitive type of tasks that can certainly signal some characteristics of autism. I have heard of parents that go to great lengths to change their homes when a child places objects in a certain order. Some parents might move the clothes out of the child's reach to a higher place in the closet. What happens next is that the child usually finds some other object to place in a certain order. The child may move to blankets or towels and carefully take the blankets or towels out of the closet to put in a certain order. The child is not usually doing this activity with a purpose. I mean he or she is not carefully placing the towels to clean out the closet or the bathroom, but rather for a feeling of comfort.

However, there is also the case that some typical developing children put things in a certain order. I have seen young children who put toys in a certain order to organize the toys, to categorize certain toys and place objects in groups as they engage their cognitive abilities.
I once saw a teacher call children to the table to sort animals to various groups on paper plates. A person should not confuse typical grouping or categorizing objects that are part of a child's development with this repetitive type of behavior when a child is putting something in a particular order with no real purpose or learning objective.

Chapter 4
Social Interaction Concerns

Social interaction delays are common among many children. Parents may have concerns the child is not sharing toys with others or that the child is aggressive with other children. However, the school psychologist and other clinic professionals may be watching if the child engages or refuses direct requests. There may be other concerns related to avoidance behaviors and avoiding eye contact when engaging with a child. It is noted that some children totally avoid eye contact, while other children only avoid eye contact occasionally. Social awareness is an important part of understanding socialization delays or autism concerns. Social interaction can be as simple as reaching for a toy or making social contact with a person.

The professionals are looking to see if the child has an awareness of others or if the child is withdrawn from any type of social or play experiences. Professionals are looking to discuss the child's play interaction skills and to see if the child has appropriate or inappropriate play skills. For example, is the child playing with only the toy or is he or she using the toy to interact and communicate with others in the child's play experiences? Sometimes parents will notice these social interaction concerns, but at other times school psychologists and other professionals need to point out unusual or nonresponsive social interaction exchanges.

REFUSAL OF DIRECT REQUESTS

Parent Concern

My child will not complete anything and he just turns away when an activity is placed in front of him.

A School Psychologist's Perspective

Sometimes the refusal of direct requests is related to the lack of social interaction and communication skills of the child. He or she may go to a corner of a room, sit under a table or find a private area to complete a simple puzzle or block activity. The child may be taking time to warm up to the professional and if the activity is placed in front of the child, he or she may complete it later in the assessment. There have been times when professionals have conducted home observations and approach the child with a request. The response to the professionals can be varied, but this allows the professionals to see how the child reacts to the direct request.

In one home observation the school psychologist and special education teacher are discussing concerns and before they even try to interact with the child, he or she has disappeared in the bedroom showing no interest in social contact. I conducted an office assessment one time where the child simply wanted no part of any direct request. A drawing activity was presented to the young girl and she walked away with no eye contact or interest. Later in the assessment, a puzzle was presented to the girl and she simply took the puzzle after is was placed on the floor and sat in the corner with her back to me. The refusal of direct requests seems to be a common occurrence for children with autism concerns.

AVOIDANCE BEHAVIORS

Parent Concern

My child seems to avoid making eye contact and just looks away when I am trying to make social contact.

A School Psychologist's Perspective

Children with autism may exhibit many different types of avoidance behaviors in social and school settings. Of course, eye contact is often discussed as something to avoid and can be avoided by looking away when a person tries to make social contact with the child, calling on him or her in class or at home. But, there are many other avoidance behaviors that may surface in autism such as avoiding certain foods. It is not uncommon for children with autism characteristics to have avoidance of various textures of food. Some parents have mentioned that their children only eat cereal without milk or only certain brands of food products.

Avoidance behavior can come in many forms such as avoiding group situations or being extremely fearful or certain situations or objects. It is not unusual for parents of children with autism characteristics to share of avoidance for hair cuts, vacuum cleaners, household objects (e.g. garbage disposals or blenders) or a character on a television show. Some children have toileting accidents and issues because they want to avoid the toilet as they are scared of the flushing noise. Some children avoid the 'dark,' but this characteristic is often seen in children without autism as well.

UNAWARENESS OF OTHERS

Parent Concern

My child just seems to be totally unaware of other kids in the day care room.

A School Psychologist's Perspective

When a child exhibits behavior where he or she shows an unawareness of other people it can cause one to look at and examine the child's motives. Of course, this may be a developmental delay where the child lacks social skills. It could be a behavior related concern as the child has a short attention span and be unaware of others as he is easily distracted. There could be hearing issues as the child does not seem to hear when others speak to him or her or fails to turn and look at who might be entering the room. However, some parents I have interviewed indicated that their children had positive hearing tests in the normal range and the child's behavior was more likely related to his or her awareness of others.

Children with autism characteristics may be in a room with a group of people and be totally unaware of people entering and leaving the room. The child may not make eye contact, fail to turn or look who may be entering the room, may not respond to his name when called or even acknowledge a person at all. I used to know a nurse who would clap her hands behind young children with autism and they seldom would turn around to look at who was making the noise. The child may be more interested in the toy he or she is playing with and become more aware of the toy or object than the person in the room.

INAPPROPRIATE PLAY

Parent Concern

My child plays by himself and always plays with the same toy.

A School Psychologist's Perspective

Play patterns are noticed when assessing children with autism characteristics. Of course typically developing children would show a variety of play patterns that may include symbolic or dramatic play where the child transforms an object to something or someone else. It can also include collaboration in play with turn taking and sharing experiences as the child uses imagination or constructive play to create new things. In examining children with autism characteristics there seems to be much less social play with peers. As a result the play observed may be solitary activities where the child is self centered and in his or her 'own world.' The child would often prefer to play with an object rather than other children.

Sometimes the child is very mechanical and takes objects apart (e.g. at times puts the objects back together again) and at other times is destructive with toys. There are also cases of parallel play where the child will play beside or near another kid, but each child is playing with his or her own toy or activity. Parents often report these children stay on the edge in social activities. Families have shared there are many siblings and relatives in the home, but the child still keeps to him or herself. The child may also focus on only one type of toy (e.g. dinosaurs) or one category of or type of objects (e.g. only play with blue blocks).

WITHDRAWN CHILD

Parent Concern

My child must be autistic since she is so withdrawn from the other children at preschool.

A School Psychologist's Perspective

The professional has to really observe the child closely as some children present as autistic at first with a withdrawn type of personality. Later in the assessment, the child may warm up and actually present him or herself as a child with transition difficulties. The delayed child with transition difficulties needs support in being comfortable with new situations. This is why some teachers have free play when the children arrive in day care or preschool. It is important to note that some children who are withdrawn may be extremely shy and are actually delayed in social skills so social interaction play experiences may help them come out of their shyness and learn the skills to socially interact with peers.

A child with autism can appear in more than one way. Some children with autistic characteristics will avoid other children playing and simply withdraw from a group situation by playing with a toy in solitary play. A child with autism characteristics can avoid play and interaction so much that he or she may simply turn his or her back to the other children and teachers in class. Other children will play near another child, but stay on the edge of the group. The withdrawn child with autism characteristics may not want to participate in circle time or group learning activities, but the child may still be listening as he or she wanders off to the side of the classroom.

PLAY INTERACTION

Parent Concern

My child does not play with other children so I think he has autism. He seems to be shy and is slow to warm up to others.

A School Psychologist's Perspective

There are several reasons a child may lack play interaction skills. First, many children have been home and have had limited play experiences with other children. Second, a child with language delays or just a few words lacks the language skills to invite others to play or initiate conversations with other children. Sometimes children with autistic concerns almost appear to show they are engaging in play interaction, but on closer look they are actually engaging in 'self talk.' The self talk is often directed to an object rather than a person.

An example would be a young girl playing in a kitchen with another girl and they are both preparing food. One child says 'look at my cookie' as she shows the cookie to the other girl and this would be an appropriate play interaction. The other girl is cutting a piece of toy pizza and she is only looking at the pizza and says 'I cut pizza.' This child is interacting with the pizza and engaging in self talk as she directs her conversation to the object and not the other girl who she almost looks to be interacting with in creative play. Observation of play experiences provides a crucial amount of information in determining if a child has autism or just delayed social and play experiences.

REFUSAL TO CONNECT WITH GROUPS

Parent Concern

My child does not go over to join the group activities at preschool.

A School Psychologist's Perspective

When a child refuses to play socially or connect with group activities if could be a characteristic of autism. However, it could be that a child has some delays and just lacks the social or communication skills to join in groups. Some children have limited language skills and would not initiate conversation in a play activity. Some group activities are more interactive, while some toys like puzzles are completed more individually by the child. Some preschool students are very shy and parents have explained they lack social skills because of very limited play experiences where the child was at home with adults.

I think it is important to see that some children need a longer time to warm up and get involved in play groups. Children with autism characteristics could do one of several things.

Children with autism concerns may simply ignore the other children in the groups or simply turn away wanting no part of social contact. Other children may not join in the group circle time activity, but go off and pick up a toy to avoid the total interaction of the teacher and other children. Sometimes joining in group activities can be related to interest in a topic. If a child loves dinosaurs then he or she may participate, but when other subjects and topics are introduced the child may totally avoid the group participation.

REFUSAL TO ANSWER QUESTIONS

Parent Concern

My child never answers any question I ask her, it seems like she tunes me out.

A School Psychologist's Perspective

There are several possibilities that a child might refuse to answer a question. A child with autism concerns may simply not respond to an oral request and a person would almost think the child can't hear. However, many students I have worked with have excellent hearing. Speech delayed children may not respond to a question (even if they know the answer) because the child lacks the vocabulary to come up with the words to express a thought. The child with autism characteristics will sometimes show no respond to any of the adults asking questions. The child continues to play with his or her toy or electronic device and you could ask the child multiple questions without a response. It is sometimes difficult for parents to understand a child not responding to questions.

A child may also be selective and answer a question from a parent or relative, but refuse to answer a question from an unfamiliar person. Sometimes children lack socialization skills to interact with the person answering the question. A child may not answer a question because he or she does understand what the adult is talking about. The child may have limited cognitive abilities and does not understand the concepts being presented to him or her. The child may not have been exposed to the topic he or she is being asked about so there is a pause, delay or simply no response to the question.

Chapter 5
Unusual Behavior Concerns

The areas of strange or unusual behavior concerns should not be taken lightly. However, some of the behaviors may be viewed as delayed while other behaviors signify more deep seated issues and concerns. There may be reasons for an unusual behavior. Some behaviors can be as simple as chewing on clothing to extreme strange acting behaviors. Sometimes parents just overlook a strange behavior because they are used to it and have accepted it as a habit or something the child does that is just a little unusual. The professional is trying to explore the behaviors of the child and understand if the strange behaviors are sensory related or caused by internal feelings or possibly external or environmental factors. The school psychologist wants to see if the unusual behaviors are from lack of understanding as in low cognitive abilities or if the confusion is related to communication and social issues.

A school psychologist may recognize that some children are confused by a request. The other component of an unusual behavior is some behaviors are related to sensory issues. The school psychologist may be looking at sound sensory issues and how the child responds to sounds in the environment. Touching sensory experiences may open up strange behaviors related to the feel of objects. Oral sensory issues really stand out as some children mouth toys and objects in the environment. The professionals are trying to help parents see if these behaviors are a reason for concern and look at strategies to help the child.

CHEWING ON CLOTHING OR CLOTH ITEMS

Parent Concern

My foster child constantly chews on his shirt and blanket, should I be concerned?

A School Psychologist's Perspective

A child who has the behavior of chewing on clothing may show some autism tendencies, but may also just be delayed. Really young children tend to show this tendency more than others. I recently looked at many photos of one of my twins chewing on her clothing. However, when she had her tonsils and adenoids come out the chewing on clothing stopped immediately. At the same time, children chew on clothes for a variety of reasons.

Certainly one can see that a child who has nervous type behaviors and may chew on clothing because he or she is stressed out by a family situation. Sometimes, the child is bored and chewing on clothing as something to do or at other times it might be just a low motor tone in the face and chewing gum might help the child grow out of it. When looking at the area of autism, a parent would want to consider if the child is chewing on clothing as a sensory experience. If the child is chewing on clothing to repetitively feel the sensation of wet clothing then this behavior may be related to autism. However, one might also consider if a child has mouth pain and perhaps he or she is cutting teeth and chewing on the clothing may just be a comfort for the pain. One cannot forget that there is also the child searching for attention by chewing on clothes and so some parents avoid addressing it as not to draw attention to the issue.

CONFUSION FROM A REQUEST

Parent Concern

I ask my child to pick up his toys and he seems totally confused by the request.

A School Psychologist's Perspective

Confusion comes in many forms for children. Sometimes the delayed behavior of confusion is from the adults giving inconsistent messages to the child. One parent may be telling the child 'no' and another parent tells him or her that it is 'ok' to do the same thing. The child's confusion may come from a parent changing the guidelines. When someone says 'don't drink out of the milk carton' one time and another time says 'it's ok to drink from the milk carton' the person is sending mixed messages. Sometimes the child is confused from turmoil in the household.

The behavior of children with autism may be in a state of confusion. The child may lack communication skills so expressing needs and wants is confusing. The child may also struggle with social interaction skills so a simple task such as playing with other children at the park is confusing for some children because they don't know the skills to initiate play with others. Confusion can come when a child has stereotype repetitive behaviors and does a task over and over again. Other children may become confused as they don't know why a child is lining up the toys and spinning the object over and over again. The child repeating the task gets frustrated because the other children do not understand his or her reactions or responses.

STRANGE ACTING BEHAVIOR

Parent Concern

My child does strange things, he plays with his poop and makes a mess in the bathroom.

A School Psychologist's Perspective

Acting strangely could be many things in the areas of mental health or an educational concern, so one must be cautious in immediately thinking this atypical behavior is autism or some other criteria for mental illness. There are issues where a child could be just delayed in self help or daily living skills. The child may not understand how to wipe or clean him or her self properly. The child may not know the bathroom routines or need assistance in wiping and learning personal hygiene. A child may act strangely to gain attention for his or her needs to be recognized. If a child is abused or neglected they may do something outrageous as a sign for help. A child may make a mess or go to the bathroom on the floor to signal others there are some problems he or she needs help with and may want to draw immediate attention to the problem. This is a powerful cry for help and in some children it is a call of desperation.

Strange behavior may occur in a child or teenager who needs to talk about a problem such as bullying or harassment. Strange behaviors may also occur when a child has some deep seated emotional and psychological issues. A child with autism may seem strange to someone who does not understand why the child repeats a task over and over. Teachers and counselors can play an important role in helping the child talk about feelings outside the home setting.

SOUND SENSORY ISSUES

Parent Concern

My child puts his hands over his ears when he hears any kind of loud noises.

A School Psychologist's Perspective

Sensory issues impact children with autism in many different ways. For one child, a sensory experience may be drastic and for another child it makes no difference to the child. One child I met many years ago would attend piano recitals as his mother was a music teacher. The boy was well behaved until the clapping came at the end of the first performance and then the child became a total wreck with tantrums. The child appeared to be fine during the playing of the many instruments and the melody of the music, but the clapping sensation over stimulated him. A surprise sound such as fireworks or a balloon popping at a party may have varied reactions for a child.

There are other sound sensory issues that bother and don't bother children. Sometimes a child immediately responds to various sounds by putting his or her hands over the ears. This is sometimes observed with the daily sounds of flushing a toilet or the sounds of a school bus or trash truck. The sound of vacuum cleaner can cause a big reaction in some children. On the other hand, a young child may enjoy the repetitive nature of sounds. A child may flush the toilet over and over again to hear the sound of the water. The world of sound impacts children differently, so a parent and professional will want to observe the child's responses and how it is related to communication and social interaction.

ORAL SENSORY ISSUES

Parent Concern

My child puts every toy she plays with in her mouth.

A School Psychologist's Perspective

Other types of sensory issues may involve the child tasting or licking objects. There have been numerous times I have requested young children to build with blocks and they would lick the blocks. Parents have noted that some children lick all of the hot seasoning from the snacks and never eat the actual snack. In high schools, there have been incidents where a high school student with autism would lick the lotion on a staff members hand or try to lick the scented shampoo in someone's hair.

It is important to distinguish that some things are typical to lick (such as a lollipop) and some things are inappropriate to put in the mouth or lick (inedible objects). I have heard parents comment that they must closely supervise their children at all times due to the nature of things the children are putting in their mouths. Chocking and gagging on inedible items is a grave concern for many parents. Parents have commented to me over the years that children have eaten paper, stuffed toilet paper in the mouth, chew on metal or wood objects (e.g. around the coffee table) and stuff blocks and toys in the mouth. Occupational therapists are excellent in helping children with these issues and they sometimes complete a sensory assessment on the child and can make recommendations to help the family and child.

TOUCHING SENSORY ISSUES

Parent Concern

My child constantly takes off his shoes and socks and it is difficult to keep him in his shoes.

A School Psychologist's Perspective

Sometimes sensory experiences involve the feel of objects or people. You may have noticed that these students want to take off their socks and shoes and feel the carpet or flooring. Some parents just let the child run free in the home setting and other parents are concerned. This situation usually doesn't bother parents in the home setting, but when the child goes to school new issues arise. The schools and bus require children to wear shoes or foot wear for protection from diseases or stepping on sharp objects. Parents may have to explore new types of shoes that stay on longer. The school and special education teacher will have guidelines and the change for the child may be somewhat difficult at first.

I once observed a child stroking the parents' face in a way that almost seemed liked the child was pinching the parent's cheek. Upon observation the child was just enjoying the sensory experience of touching and stroking the skin. Another touching sensory observation may be the child running his or her hand over the carpet, a wall or a texture that the child will calm the child. This is especially noticed in children with autism as they feel comfort from this sensory sensation. There have been calming techniques used for some children than involve the feel of being wrapped in a blanket.

SMELLING SENSORY ISSUES

Parent Concern

My child tries to smell everything from toys to hand lotion.

A School Psychologist's Perspective

Some children who smell everything have sensory issues and could have a characteristic of autism. Smelling items could also be related to other conditions such as obsessive-compulsive disorder. However, parents have to supervise children with these strong smelling sensory issues. The child may be searching for items in the house to smell and this curiosity could be dangerous as the child tries to reach and open various products to smell without a real sense of danger. The child could have a physical reaction or outbreak to something that is hazardous. The child may have an allergic reaction or gag from the smell of an object or substance and this could require medical attention.

A child's behavior can change related to the smell of some objects. Sometimes the child can get upset by a smell and at other times go on a binge to smell everything in site. A child can also have a fear of certain smells and when in the vicinity of the smell the child reacts with crying or distraught behavior. The child may smell objects with little or no smell such as blocks or hard toys. At other times, the child may have a strong reaction to scented clay or play dough and become distracted as the teacher is trying to complete an activity. Many people do not realize that a scent stays on your hands. Anyway you look at it the sense of smell can be extremely strong in the lives of some children.

UNABLE TO SLOW DOWN

Parent Concern

My child is constantly on the move and seems unable to slow himself down.

A School Psychologist's Perspective

When a child seems wound up and unable to slow down some people would suspect autism. However, this characteristic could be related to several other conditions. Many people would tend to think if a child can't slow down they may have tendencies to have some type of attention deficit hyperactivity disorder. However, this difficulty with slowing down can also be related to an anxious or nervous behavior where the child has trouble calming down. Children from high risk home environments may show this 'unable to slow down' type of behavior because they are unsure of the home and family situation. In this case, the child is just reacting to the stressors and challenges he or she is faced with in their personal situations. A social worker recommendation or a special day care program can be referred to help the child deal with these personal issues.

I would suspect that if this type of behavior is related to autism it would be connected to other issues. One example of this would be inappropriate play where the child does not slow down to play. The child just moves from toy to toy without any purpose with the toys. These children tend to make huge messes in the classroom and preschools. This is one of the first signs that shows up to the parent and the preschool is recommending that the parent take the child in to a clinic and get him or her tested for autism or developmental delays.

Chapter 6
Daily Living Concerns

Many parents are more concerned with toileting issues than any other daily living concerns. Toileting issues are a concern for the professional because the child has to indicate or let others know of his or her intent to go to the bathroom. If the child is delayed or not communicating this intent then the question is whether the child doesn't know the toileting routines or if there is an avoidance to indicate the child's needs. A deficit in daily living skills can signal if the child has delays or really struggles with the intent to get his or her daily living needs met. There are other daily living concerns such as using eating utensils, emotional difficulties, uneven skill development and unawareness of danger.

Another daily living skill is the child's ability to use eating utensils. Since many children with autism finger feed foods and avoid using eating utensils this will be observed closely by professionals. Emotional difficulties related to tantrums are sometimes examined in the daily living are if the tantrums are related to self-help skills. The child may have uneven skill development such as being advanced in one area (e.g. knowing colors and numbers) and delayed in another area (e.g. toileting skills). A big daily living concern is unawareness of dangerous situations. This can be acting without thinking about the consequences of the child's actions. It can also be the child who escapes locked doors as he or she learns to get out of locked doors. Daily living routines are noticed by professionals as they see how the child maneuvers the home and community environments.

EATING UTENSIL DIFFICULTIES

Parent Concern

My child can't use a spoon, he only eats finger foods and refuses to pick up a fork or spoon.

A School Psychologist's Perspective

There can be more to the picture of using eating utensils than meets the eye. It could be just a stage the child is going through and he or she might be showing a preference for finger foods at that time. The child could outgrow this stage. On the other hand, there could be motor planning issues of just difficulty with fine motor issues. Some children need modifications, while other children need help in developing their fine motor skills. I have also heard occupational and physical therapists comment that many child have the motor strength to perform the task of holding a spoon or fork, but lack the opportunity because the parents or older siblings are doing most of the tasks for the child.

Children with autism and sensory issues sometimes need specialized forks and spoons with a variety of grips to encourage utensil use. In educational settings, there can be many opportunities (stories, finger plays and songs) to help the young child gain hands on experience, direct examples and role playing in using eating utensils in the classroom. Several educational professionals may be involved in this process as there could be developmental delays or occupational or motor issues.

TOILETING DIFFICULTIES

Parent Concern

My child is not toilet trained so does that mean she had autism? I have tried everything and nothing seems to be working for her.

A School Psychologist's Perspective

In autism assessments, there are a number of daily living difficulties that can be explored. Of course, toileting and toileting difficulties are often mentioned. Partially the reason for this is that when a child is being toilet trained he or she has to let someone know the diaper is soiled or ask to go to the bathroom or toilet by indicating it in some way. Children with autism would have difficulty doing this because they have a hard time communicating their wants and needs. However, children with speech and language delays may also have a difficult time communicating their needs.

Although, toileting difficulties is one characteristic listed on some autism types of checklists, it is certainly not the overriding and determining factor as to whether the child has autism. Many children with developmental delays have difficulties with toileting, so it is only one small component of a much broader picture of the child. It must be emphasized that toileting difficulties present in many children with delays. The professional is looking more at the child's willingness or ability to indicate a need to toilet or let the parent know he or she is soiled.

Unawareness of Dangerous Situations

Parent Concern

My child does not seem to be aware that she does many dangerous things.

A School Psychologist's Perspective

Another area mentioned was that of an awareness of dangerous situations. Children with autism may have difficulty being able to recognize dangerous situations. This can involve risk taking behaviors like touching hot stoves or a hot surface. However, it can also involve things such as recognizing a stranger and the danger of getting into a car or leaving with someone the child doesn't know. In addition, there are also environmental dangers as the child may be unaware of cars in the street, taking off seatbelts, staying on the sidewalk and being aware of general dangers in society. Another concern is the child is so self absorbed in what he or she is doing that the child becomes unaware of danger.

It is important to note that just because a child has risk taking behaviors it should not automatically be assumed that he or she has autism. There are many other behavioral concerns and mental illnesses that also involve risk taking behaviors. Sometimes a young child is being manipulative with his parents and trying to see how much he can get away with before he is stopped from dangerous activities. It takes observation and information from the parent to help determine if the child is aware or unaware of dangerous situations.

ESCAPING OR UNLOCKING DOORS

Parent Concern

My child has unlocked the door and left the house in the middle of the night.

A School Psychologist's Perspective

Parents of children with autism often describe these children as being 'master artists' of unlocking doors and escaping from the house. This is frightening for parents and it is a shock for parents when a child leaves the house in the middle of the night. The parent may not even realize the child is out of the house and the child could come back and crawl into bed without the parents ever suspecting the child has left the house. At other times, a neighbor working the late night or early morning shift will see the child on the street and bring the child home to the parents.

A person may ask 'how can a child escape-can't you get a better lock on the door?' One parent shared how they moved the lock higher on the door so it would be out of reach for the child. The child was still able to figure out how to get out of the house. The child can use a variety of methods for getting out of the house. The child learns quickly to get on a chair or get a stick to open a high lock. Parents have also mentioned they have changed the codes on the alarm systems in their houses. However, children with autism often have a good number sense and quickly memorize the new code or numbers to open an electronic alarm system.

EMOTIONAL DIFFICULTIES

Parent Concern

My son has so many tantrums he must be autistic.

A School Psychologist's Perspective

Emotional difficulties seem to come up in autism evaluations sometimes as a parent confuses a child with socialization and behavioral issues with a child who has autism characteristics. Some of the autism parent checklists ask parents about temper tantrums and if the child gets upsets from routine changes or when asked to take a direction. Most school psychologists and teachers are looking at the 'intent' of the child's behavior. A behavior rating scale, in addition to the autism parent rating type of scales may provide more helpful information to the school psychologist.

On a parent autism type of rating scale, a child may have difficulty by becoming upset or frustrated if his or her needs or requests are not met on demand. However, a child such as this may also have socialization issues in the hyperactivity area as he or she has trouble waiting to take a turn. One has to observe if the temper tantrum is an intent to get the child's way or simply a lack of frustration because of a communication or social interaction difficulty. It is worthy to fully examine these emotional difficulties to see if there are socialization/behavioral issues and is just a child having transition concerns, preschool separation issues or hyperactivity distractions rather than common socialization and communication difficulties.

UNEVEN SKILL DEVELOPMENT

Parent Concern

My child is so smart he knows all his colors, numbers and letters. How can you suggest that a child this 'bright' has autism?

A School Psychologist's Perspective

A common characteristic of children with autism is uneven skill development. This is different from recognizing the strengths and weaknesses of a child. In uneven skill development, a child may be brilliant in math, but have a major delay in his or her daily living or social skills. The child may have wonderful cognitive abilities, but lacks the social and pragmatic skills to communicate that information and knowledge to others. This a big signal to professionals assessing the child that there is a clear difference in how the child's skills are developing.

Sometimes educational professionals may not recognize these skill development issues immediately. For example, a young bright child goes to a preschool, the staff immediately love this child as he or she knows all of his or her colors, letters and numbers. The child may not be a trouble maker and gets a toy as he or she plays quietly by him or herself. The staff may love having the child in class because he or she is not a trouble maker. The staff may overlook that the child is not communicating and socially interacting with the other children in the classroom. The most questionable cases of autism seem to be around the high functioning children with autism.

CLEANLINESS ISSUES

Parent Concern

My child does not wash her hands after eating, should I be concerned?

A School Psychologist's Perspective

Young children are playful so of course they get dirty after playing in the mud, using paint and eating messy foods. Sometimes children forget to wash their hands or properly clean up and this would be typical for most young children. A child can learn clean up skills several ways. For example, child may learn clean up from peers or other children. After all, when your friends think it is fun to wash hands then you may think it is fun to try it as well. The preschool teacher may also have specific objectives she or he is working on in class when cleanliness skills are demonstrated or the steps for washing hands are reviewed in the preschool classroom.

If a child has autism, there can be concerns about the child's awareness that he or she is even dirty or unclean. However, what I see more often is the opposite. I have seen parents of children with autism characteristics report the child always cleans his or her face after eating and will clean the table and food area. The child sees cleaning up as a repetitive type of task and there is comfort and satisfaction in being clean. Often children who have delays in the daily living area may just lack skills and experiences in cleaning themselves. Some children have not had demands or expectations put on them to clean themselves or pick up messy areas. Sometimes this is cultural or gender based in some countries where there is not an expectation to clean up.

CHANGES IN DAILY PLANS

Parent Concern

My child has a bad reaction when we change any routine or the way we do things at home.

A School Psychologist's Perspective

Adaptability to new situations, plans and routines is part of life. It is a practical way of living and everything in life is not done a certain way every day. Some children have adaptability issues because they are clingy toward the parents and have had limited play experiences with other children. In this case, the more exposure to others and opportunities to see other children interact will help the child. This can make the first day of preschool a miserable experience for the child and the parent. Sometimes parents over react to the child's response and immediately pull the child from the preschool. It is not uncommon for children to cry the first few days of preschool, but most children adjust fine after they are adapted to preschool and make some new friends.

A child with autism characteristics may resist a change in plans because it disrupts the order and precise routine the child needs for self-stimulatory behavior. This precise routine of the child helps him or her manage emotions and or sensory input. At times, there is a severe reaction to change and the child will hurt him or herself or others. This child may not be able to handle this new change without support. Sometimes parents are encouraged for their children to ride a bus to school since it seems to make a smoother transition than when a parent drops or leaves the child at school.

Chapter 7
Ten Parent Concerns

PARENTAL CONCERN #1
TYPE OF REFERRAL

The parent must consider the type of referral or the reason that autism concerns were brought up for evaluation. This can happen for a variety of reasons. Sometimes another family member has autism and the parent is seeing similar characteristics or patterns in his or her child. Sometimes, the referral comes from early childhood intervention case workers or developmental specialists who have been working with the child and parents for months. These workers start documenting concerns and recording observations to provide reasons for a referral. Sometimes a head start or title one teacher notices some behaviors or unusual characteristics that concern them in the classroom setting and a referral is recommended.

I think it is important to understand that sometimes the developmental specialist or teacher working with the child never really mentions the word 'autism' to the parents. The teacher may say the child has speech delays or concerns because the child is not talking in class. A developmental specialist working in the home may tell the parent the child has some 'sensory issues' and recommends a further evaluation of the child. Therefore, when a team mentions an eligibility of autism to the parents it can be a shock or an unexpected outcome. It is important for the parent to ask questions and get clarification along the way about the referral.

PARENTAL CONCERN #2
DISTORTED INFORMATION

I once had parents say they wanted to get a child tested for autism at the clinic because the child already had a diagnosis of autism. However the diagnosis did not come from a medical doctor or trained professional. After questioning the parent, it turned out that the parent had taken an online questionnaire on some website and determined the child had autism from the website. Although, the child may have had some of the symptoms of the autism from the questionnaire it should be viewed with caution. Many of the websites will indicate that these characteristics could also be developmental delays of the child and that the information is used as a screener and is not a full evaluation. The websites often suggest that parents seek a full assessment or evaluation to determine if the child has autism.

Parents must be aware that this limited information would not necessarily be a good predictor of whether the child has autism. After all, no one is observing the child or seeing how the child interacts and communicates with people. In addition, a multidisciplinary team assessment will allow several different professionals to look at the child and see the child from different angles. Professionals don't always agree on their views of the child. Sometimes additional observations are made in the home to obtain a better picture of the child. An evaluation or assessment for a young child will look at multiple areas and then it should provide a profile of the child's strengths and weaknesses. Even a child with autism will generally have strengths that can be built on and weaknesses that can be addressed in schools.

PARENTAL CONCERN #3
TIMING OF REFERRAL

Parents need to be aware that characteristics of autism often present themselves prior to the age of three. These traits and characteristics are presented in very young children so people working with the child may start pointing out these traits as the child attends preschool, church activities or recreational activities. Sometimes a child has been sheltered at home with no preschool or early childhood intervention and when they arrive at a diagnostic clinic at age 5 or 6, the autism characteristics may be noted as eligibility is determined. At times, a school psychologist may get an unusual referral that an eighteen year old senior in high school is referred for an autism assessment. This would be a little suspicious if the child has been attending the public schools for twelve years and no professional has pointed out concerns prior to this age.

On the other hand, students coming from developing countries to the United States may not have had any formal assessments to determine if autism characteristics exist. As well, some students are home schooled for many years and the parents have not sought to bring the child out of the home into social or educational settings. It may be the first time the child has been formally assessed for autism at a later age. Parents may have sheltered the child (intentionally or unintentionally) and now want the older child to go to school. Parents may not realize the child does not have the communication and social skills to immediately function in a regular education setting. The referral is the first step in a process with lots of planning and decisions for the child's educational future.

PARENTAL CONCERN #4
LIMITED CHARACTERISTICS OF AUTISM

One concern that some parents have struggled with is when autism is diagnosed based on very limited characteristics. I once knew a little girl and when her mother told me she had autism I was very surprised. After all the young girl 'waved and said hello' when I saw her at the roller skating rink. The girl also told me that she would save the seat in front of her at the baseball game for her friend as she left to pick up a hot dog. I have observed this young girl to have fairly good social interaction and communication skills. She was actually placed in a regular education room with very limited support in special education.

One day I asked the girl's mother, how she knew the child had autism. The mother said the girl had temper tantrums in the grocery store when she was a toddler. This seemed to be the major issue and determination in why the girl was diagnosed with autism. I admit that having temper tantrums is one trait listed on several autism evaluation instruments, but autism is a communication and social interaction disorder characterized by stereotyped behaviors. What was so much more obvious in this girl is that she had a delay in her socialization skills. In addition, many children's temper tantrums are reduced once they learn to communicate their needs and wants. In perspective, this girl was diagnosed with autism and a label was put on her based on very limited characteristics that she had temper tantrums as a toddler. Sometimes a parent looks at only one characteristic (e.g. covering ears) and assumes autism on a very limited characteristic. Parents and professionals must not base an autism eligibility on a child with very limited characteristics.

PARENTAL CONCERN #5
CULTURAL ISSUES RELATED TO AUTISM

Cultural issues can certainly play a role in determining characteristics of autism. This is especially true when second language and cultural issues creep into an assessment of a child who has recently moved to a new country, state or town. Parents must be aware of issues that would come up with a high score on an autism type of rating scale. For example, if the child is not using words and communicates by gestures, this could come across as autism characteristics. However, it may also be a child who has a speech and language delay. It could also be a second language learner, who needs some time to learn a new language and cultural experiences.

These cultural issues can also be seen in the play area. For example, I once had a child and his sister who moved to a new country. The children had not been exposed to electronic types of toys that made noises and had bright lights. As a result, the children acted fearful of toys, refused to play with toys, covered their ears and would not even touch the toys. Sure some of the characteristics of inappropriate play with toys could be construed as autism, but they could also be from a child who has had limited cultural experiences with toys and therefore presented as a fearful child. When there are major cultural changes (e.g. moving to a new country) or language issues (e.g. learning a new language in a short period of time) there must be caution not to confuse cultural changes with autism characteristics. There are periods of time needed to observe the child once he or she adjusts to a new situation or experience. If autism is an issue it will present itself across cultures.

PARENTAL CONCERN #6
PURPOSEFUL BEHAVIORS

During the assessment process, many clinicians are examining not only the characteristics of autism in the child, but the purposefulness of the child's behaviors. These professionals often look to see if the child has intent in their behaviors and actions. The parent must be aware that children with autism often are unaware of their surroundings and the social interaction as they communicate with others.

Children who are aware of their intent and purpose may be more likely to have socialization or behavioral issues. This is examined in how children play with others. For example, a young boy hitting his brother to make him cry and when the brother runs to mom, the young boy takes his brother's toy. This young boy would have purpose in hitting his brother to obtain the toy.

A child talking on a toy telephone would be playing appropriately with the telephone and using it for a purpose. On the other hand, a child who takes every toy off the shelf and does not play for any length of time with any of them shows no purpose or interest in the toy. Sometimes a child who has been quiet for most of the assessment will ask to go to a fast food restaurant at the end of the assessment. This child is showing that he or she was aware of being rewarded for completing the assessment tasks and activities. Speech therapists have on occasion commented that a child who parents report is not speaking, is actually purposefully not speaking since others wait on him or her and meet every need the child requests.

PARENTAL CONCERN #7
INCONSISTENT LIVING PATTERNS

In conducting multidisciplinary assessments, it should be noted that the school psychologist likes to review how the child behaves and interacts across settings and with people at different times and places. If the child is great at home and church, but only has problems in the day care setting, it might be that the day care is not a good fit for the child. If the child is great in the first part of an autism assessment, then becomes fussy at the very end of the assessment, it might be because the child is hungry or tired. Some parents will say a child is fine, but a child can also be slow to warm up to a new situation. The child many also have difficulty with transitions in multiple settings. When a child walks into a clinic to be assessed he or she may think it is a doctor's office where they will be getting a shot. Once the child realizes the clinic has toys he or she may warm up to a new setting with a greater comfort level.

I have also worked in cities with casinos where parents worked split shifts and had irregular sleep patterns. Children, themselves can have irregular sleep schedules where they stay up late one day and get up early the next day and have difficulty adjusting to routines and schedules. Sometimes a child is assessed on two different days and the professionals can see the difference in the child's behavior. Parents and professionals must examine if the inability to adjust to routines is because of autism or other issues such as the home environment, work schedules and inconsistent living patterns. Inconsistent living patterns can certainly account for child's fluctuating behavior and actions.

PARENT CONCERN #8
INCONSISTENT PARENT RATINGS

Parents need to be aware that numerous parent rating scales are used in the assessment process. This is to get a picture of the child's strengths and weaknesses. The professionals usually try to conduct direct assessments with the child to really see where the child's abilities and skills fall. Sometimes behavioral issues make it difficult to directly assess a child so parent interview and observation are important in the assessment. At times, parent ratings can give inconsistent information. For example, some parents respond 'yes' the three year old does everything even an 8 or 9 year old child does. For example, the parent may say the child picks up toys, but in the assessment the child refuses twice to pick up the toys. The professional may want to discuss these responses with the parent to get a more accurate picture of the child's skills and abilities.

On the other hand, there are parents who rate the child so low that it seems the child can't do anything at all. For instance, one parent said the child had really low comprehension of language and cognitive abilities. In direct assessment, the child was extremely high in these areas. Parent rating scales had to be discussed with parents to clarify some of the low rating responses.

Sometimes inexperience and motives of the parents' play a role in 'cautionary' ratings by parents. The young parent may answer 'yes' to everything to get the child in a program and get what they think is 'free preschool' or just lack the understanding of how active a young child is at 2-3 years of age and that some behavior is just typical for a child of that age.

PARENTAL CONCERN # 9
MEDICAL CONCERNS RELATED TO AUTISM

Parents may not realize that a medical condition or medical concerns are an important part of the multidisciplinary team assessment of the child. Medical information is an important part of exploring the whole picture of the child. Using a nurse or medical professional on an autism assessment team can be beneficial. Since the nurse has had different training than teachers, school psychologists, speech therapists and parents she or he can contribute to the medical aspects of the development of the child. The nurse can help the parent clarify some medical conditions that may or may not be related to autism. An example would be the autism characteristic of toe walking. Toe walking is a characteristic of autism, but can also be related to neuromuscular diseases, cerebral palsy, muscle coordination, problems with Achilles tendons or other muscular disorders.

One child I observed would flap hands, but the nurse helped the parent see that it may be a motor delay as the child seemed to have involuntary movements. The nurse recommended a genetic evaluation to follow-up with the child and doctor. Especially in cases of adoption when much of the medical history is not known any additional information is helpful. As the assessment process continues parents may reveal a family medical condition to the nurse that is not revealed in the other parts of the assessment process. The nurse can then evaluate if the medical condition is related to the behavior and communication of the child. In addition, there are a number of medical syndromes where children have a variety of characteristics that may or may not be related to autism.

PARENTAL CONCERN #10
THE INTROVERTED CHILD AND AUTISM

Parents must not mistakenly identify an introverted and shy child as one who has autism. Some children I have assessed as a school psychologist are just kind of shy, quiet and introverted by the nature of their personalities. These children don't care to talk a lot and prefer to keep to themselves. However, once they warm up to a person the child will often follow directions, respond to social requests and even use social greetings such as 'hi' and 'bye.' I also think it is important as a parent to see that some children are much more verbal than other children. I noticed that in the behavior of my own twins. One twin is somewhat shy and when her friends ask her to play she would just respond with a 'yes' or 'no' response. The other twin would suggest games to play and immediately engage in social interaction.

This introverted child is different from a child with autism, who is starring off into space, not responding to his or her name and not interacting with other children. Similar characteristics between the introverted child and the child with autism may be that neither of them initiate conversations and often use gestures to obtain the objects they want to use. As a parent, one must see the bigger picture of how the introverted child communicates and socially interacts with other people. The child with autism may not always engage in communication and social exchanges or may have limited contact with others. Introverted children may choose to be alone, but they often have the ability to communicate their needs when they need their needs met.

Chapter 8
Ten Professional Concerns

PROFESSIONAL CONCERN # 1
TYPE OF TRAINING

Professionals assessing autism come from a variety of backgrounds and therefore training is very diverse. A parent cannot make assumptions about the experience and training of professionals. For example, there have been cases where medical doctors have written the word 'autism' on a prescription pad and given it to the parent. After questioning the parent about the evaluation, it was noted that the doctor did a ten minute appointment in the waiting room area. Most doctor reports have very little information and practically no assessments to make an autism determination. It is worthy to note that some doctors have not even completed one college course in child development.

My point is that sometimes parents get more helpful information from school psychologists and early childhood diagnostic centers where teachers, school psychologists and speech therapists have had years of training working with young children with autism. These professionals can spot unusual behaviors, communication patterns, play skills and social interaction skills from years of exposure working with young children. Some staff have had specialized training in autism and can help with strategies to design a helpful school plan for the child as he or she transitions into a preschool or school program. These professionals can also help with behavioral strategies to assist with the early intervention process.

PROFESSIONAL CONCERN #2
TYPE OF AUTISM ASSESSMENT

Parents must be aware of the type of autism assessment being used with the child. One parent mentioned the doctor conducted an MRI to diagnose autism, but some of these MRI techniques are still being researched on young children. Autism is a communication and social interaction type of disorder. If this is the case, then wouldn't it also be necessary to observe the child and interview the parents about the child's communication patterns, social interaction skills and stereotyped behaviors. A useful approach is for the parents to receive information about the child from more than one professional. The school psychologist is important for looking at the child's cognitive abilities and adaptive skills, but the speech therapist is equally valuable in assessing the communication, pragmatic and social skills of the child. Occupational and physical therapists can assist with motor assessments and modifications in the school environment. Teachers can help in explaining the educational services provided in the schools to help the child. All of these teams help the parent understand the assessment process.

For some parents the rating types of scales for autism can be useful, but at other times are flawed if a parent overrates or underrates behaviors. Sometimes the school psychologists have to point out to parents the obvious behaviors presented during the assessment. A parent may say 'no' the child does not flap hands or toe walk, but when the school psychologist points it out to the parent, he or she may say 'I never noticed that before now.' Home observations may be needed to provide additional information and answer questions in the assessment process. Parents and professionals working together can provide information in a useful exchange approach.

PROFESSIONAL CONCERN #3
TYPE OF SETTING

Some parents will explain the reason the child is acting unusual is because the assessment room is a new setting and the child doesn't act this way at home. The parent wants to justify that the child can do some things better in a familiar environment than in an unfamiliar environment with an unfamiliar person. However, the world is not a perfect place where everything is always done a certain way with a certain person. The professional is looking to see it the child has some consistency in working in a new surrounding with a different person. The benefit of multidisciplinary team assessments is to look at a child at different times and settings with different professionals. This is really important in the school setting when there are often changes in surroundings. The teacher may be out and there is a long term substitute teacher for the class or even a substitute bus driver who does not know the route home. The school psychologist wants to see if skills are transferable when working with a new person in a different setting.

School psychologists with more specialized training often go to the home to conduct an autism observation where they conduct a semi-structured type of observation, play games with the child and anecdotally document the child's communication, reciprocal social interaction, play and stereotyped behaviors. This assessment can be helpful in determining the probability of autism when parent rating scales and instruments don't always agree or the rating scales net a 'possibly' type of rating of autism. There are times when one autism type of rating scale has a highly likelihood of autism and another scale has a low likelihood of autism. The home observation can be one deciding factor on how the child communicates and responds in a familiar environment.

Professional Concern #4
Type of Social Risk Factors

We live in a changing world where there are risk factors from the social conditions that impact the behavior and communication of a child. A number of social risk factors can interplay with autism characteristics such as children with unstable home environments, numerous foster care placements, family histories of addiction, mental health issues or family medical history. As a result of these social factors professionals may get a high rating of autism characteristics related to having tantrums, being fearful of things, withdrawal types of behaviors, aggressive behaviors toward others and even self injury types of behaviors. It is important to see the cause of some of these behaviors is related to difficult home situations and environments that cause stress on the child. Sometimes when a foster placement is made and the child is in a more stable situation the behaviors and characteristics of the child may improve. These social risk factors can play a powerful role in the child's behavior and should be examined closely in the assessment.

The professional must look at these contributing social risk factors in relation to the assessment checklists, parent interview and the actual observation of the child. In determining autism, it is not just one factor or one area, it is a multitude of characteristics that present the child with a strong possibility of having autism. A few atypical types of behaviors or delays with a strong background of social risk factors may point toward social behavioral issues or mental health concerns even though an autism rating type of scale score indicated a high possibility of autism. School psychologists sometimes must conduct an individual item analysis on the rating scale to see which items come out strong and the reasons this may happen on a particular instrument.

PROFESSIONAL CONCERN #5
TYPE OF MIXED SIGNALS

Parents receive many mixed signals from professionals that confuse them as the child is being diagnosed with autism. Professionals may need to help the parent sort out these signals and guide the parents to think about new possibilities. Here are some mixed signals that parents have expressed:

> *The last evaluation (in another state) said my child has autism, but you say he doesn't have autism. I am confused.*

Professional Response: Professionals have varying views and use different instruments to diagnose or determine special education eligibility.

> *The early childhood intervention team said autism was a concern and your team doesn't even see it.*

Professional Response: The team reviewed the early intervention information, but our team has seen a more socially interactive child who is trying to communicate his needs.

> *The early learning classroom teacher said my child has autism and to get it checked out.*

Professional Response: Teachers have different amounts of training and education so their familiarity with autism varies. The team will evaluate the child for possible delays and or characteristics of autism.

> *A family member says my kid has autism, but I'm not sure.*

Professional Response: People and family members are looking at different aspects of the child. The multidisciplinary team will put information together from a variety of sources.

PROFESSIONAL CONCERN #6
TYPE OF OBSERVATIONS MADE

Professionals can vary in how and what they see during an observation in the evaluation process. Eye contact can be an example of this. For example, one professional will say the child avoids eye contact, while another professional says the child made eye contact with him or her. Yet, another professional will mention the child had 'fleeting eye contact,' while another person noted the child had sustained eye contact. This is also a time when parent input can be helpful. Parents are around the child more often and can make useful comments as to whether the child makes eye contact when he or she is requesting items, eating dinner and interacting in the home environment. Input may also be needed from a preschool or home observation.

Sometimes educational teams do not conduct enough observations to get a picture of the child. This is often due to time constraints, parent work hours or scheduling conflicts. A brief office assessment, a few rating scales and a short parent interview does not always provide enough information to get a full picture of the child's strengths and weaknesses. A preschool observation can help see why there are difficulties in a particular setting. It could bring out additional information on how the child interacts with other children and his or her teacher. In addition, a home observation may reveal the child's behavior was impacted from a bullying classmate, a sibling or family member. Observation notes can be extremely useful in understanding the child's communication patterns, social interaction skills, play skills and repetitive behaviors. However, interviews with the observation and a preschool teacher can help in understanding the child's behavior on a daily basis.

PROFESSIONAL CONCERN #7
TYPE OF INFORMATION REPORTED

Professionals in different areas do not always report information accurately or in the same way. When a doctor writes in a medical or professional report that a child has a hearing loss, a vision loss or certain type of syndrome this is looked at by the interdisciplinary team as they make the child's educational placement. A mistake can be devastating to the child's educational process and learning if he or she is placed in the wrong program with an incorrect diagnosis. Parents need to know when errors are spotted in an eligibility meeting, they can be changed at the meeting or in the report. This would be important if the child had a wrong allergy listed on a medical report and it would need to be corrected. In the autism assessment report it is also beneficial in getting a complete picture of the child.

The information reported may be flawed in how the information is written and in how it is actually carried out in the child's home or preschool setting. For example, in one assessment it was reported that the child was so difficult in the preschool setting that he had a one-on-one aide by his side all day. A teacher observation in the preschool setting revealed the child did not have a one-on-one assistant and was in a classroom with one teacher and eleven students. It was clear the information reported did not match the observation of the child. Therefore, this impacts the behavioral difficulties of child and how he or she may perform in a group setting with other children. In another assessment, parents reveal that a child doesn't play well with toys. A home observation indicated that the child did not have toys and therefore lacked experience playing with toys on a daily basis.

PROFESSIONAL CONCERN #8
TYPES OF BEHAVIORS REPORTED

Professionals may examine much information on behaviors to see what behaviors are reported by parents and how they are related to autism, delays or atypical types of behavior. It is not uncommon for children with autism characteristics to have difficulty with the functional communication and social skills areas. What triggers questions for many school psychologists is when there are numerous behavior areas reported in the clinically significant (or more severe) range. This would cause a school psychologist to question if this was autism or other concerns related to behavior or mental health issues.

In addition, sometimes parents rate a child high on an autism rating type of scale, but also rate the child's communication skills and socialization skills as high. Parents think it is autism because the child lines up his cars. If autism significantly impacts a child's social and communication skills, a school psychologist would not normally anticipate high scores in these areas. It signals to the school psychologist the child may have some delays or atypical types of behaviors. I would examine his or her stereotyped behaviors more closely in the areas of repetitive activities, sensory experiences or resistance to environmental change. Additional information and observations may need to be collected on this type of child. A school psychologist is looking at the types of behaviors reported and to see if there are indications of developmental delays or health issues that also need to be explored. The whole picture of the child tends to lean toward the overriding or abundant types of behaviors rather than one small behavior a child uses inconsistently.

PROFESSIONAL CONCERN# 9
TYPES OF LEGAL CONCERNS

Professionals in the area of autism seem to get more red flags over legal issues than in other areas of special education. I think this is because there is so much information on the internet. As a result, parents question professionals and are sometimes confused from being bombarded with so much information. Yet, beyond legal issues there are also emotional issues related to the idea that a child is found eligible in the autism area.

Here are some examples of issues that professionals face with regards to legal concerns:

> *The parent refused to sign the eligibility form because the parent does not want to be responsible for helping the team decide the child has autism. However, the parent may still accept school district services now or at a later time.*
>
> *The parents disagree with placement in an autism class because they feel the child is too high functioning to be with children with more severe degrees of autism and may request another Individualized Educational Plan meeting to discuss placement issues.*
>
> *The parents cannot emotionally accept the autism assessment results and continue to comment that the child has improved and the team didn't really see how well the child interacts. The parents may request another evaluation from the school district.*

There are numerous legal issues brought up in this area every day.

PROFESSIONAL CONCERN #10
TYPE OF PLACEMENT

The type of placement for the child with developmental delays or the child with autism is an important team decision. Input should be given by the team members throughout the assessment process. It is important to remember that the placement of a child in a special education program is not written in stone. If the placement is not working out the parent can request a conference with the special education teacher and school psychologist and the plan can be changed to another more suitable classroom or program. Parents may want to explore the unique ways that placements can be created at different schools in different environments.

Professionals must not only struggle with the diagnosing or assessing a child to see if he or she meets autism eligibility criteria, but these same professionals must also work out the type of placement for the child. Some placement decisions are clear cut and the child with classic autism is placed in a specialized all day autism program. At the eligibility meeting, some teams have opted to go under the category of developmental delay and continue to monitor for signs and characteristics of autism. This is done when the characteristics are not so clear. The child is placed generally in a half day program to see if these autism characteristics stand out or if the child just has some atypical quirky behaviors, but can function more like a child with delays. I am not against teams monitoring the child because a one day assessment does not always give a total picture of every child.

Chapter 9
Standout Concerns

When professionals are observing for autism there are often key characteristics that stand out. Here are a few examples that professionals may observe as they evaluate children for autism characteristics or developmental delays in the child's behavior and actions.

VOCALIZATIONS

A question professionals may ask is 'did the child show intent as he or she vocalizes and/or uses words?' The professional may consider if the vocalizations were directed toward others and it there was an attempt to communicate with the vocalizations. Sometimes vocalizations are inconsistent, odd and simply repetitive sayings that don't show if a child has knowledge of or the use of language. At other times, a child repeats a phrase, but the child is actually using the repetitive speech to process information and language. An example might be a parent who hands a child some 'fruit snacks.' The child may repeat the words 'fruit snacks' as he or she visualizes, vocalizes and processes information as he or she eats the fruit snacks.

FACIAL RESPONSES

A professional might be observing to see if a facial response or expression is used to initiate social interaction, regulate responses and/or end a social interaction. The professional may be looking to see if the child responds at all in social interaction situations. For example consider the following:

'Did the child respond to a person smiling at them or show no response at all?'

'Did the child show a facial expression responding to a pleasant or unpleasant situation?'

'Was a facial response used in connection with a vocalization to show a connection between an event and a verbalization?'

'Did the child show the facial response to a person or was the facial response only directed to an object or activity rather than the person interacting with the child?'

'Did the child use the facial response or expression to get another person's attention or initiate any type of social interaction or was the facial expression directed only to the child's personal demands or wants?'

PLAY

The professional may want to ask questions related to play such as:

'Is the child's play functional or just simply a repetitive action used over and over (e.g. spinning or moving an object back and forth)?'

'Does the child show some spontaneous pretend type of play as he or she uses objects?'

For example, just by handing a child a baby doll and a bottle one can see if the child feeds the baby or simply puts the toy down and moves to another item. I have heard many parents say that their child just simply pulls the toys off of the shelf and makes a mess of the house as the child shows no interest in any particular toy.

RESTRICTED INTEREST

It is also noticeable if the child is obsessed by one toy or object and insists only on having and playing with a specific toy. The child may also show some outburst if someone moves a toy or picks up a toy that disrupts his or her play. Restricted interest of toys can involve many things such as repetitively touching or stroking a toy, injuring him or herself with a toy, using the toy for sensory stimulation by licking or sniffing a toy or object or simply hitting a button or causing a toy to do the same action over and over without a broader perspective of play.

THE CHILD HAS DIFFICULTY WITH FEELINGS AND CAN'T ALWAYS DESCRIBE THE SITUATION

Some times atypical behaviors or delays must be looked at in the context of the child's world to see if theses are really delays or just a feeling response to a situation. A parent once told me the school called her in to request a parent conference because her son drew a picture of a historical character who had poop (small dots on the paper) coming out of his pants. The teacher immediately drew suspicion that something was wrong with the boy and that he might have autism or another serious mental disorder. The parent quickly informed the school that the child and other family members had recent bouts with stomach flu and diarrhea. The picture of the historical character just showed the child was describing his feelings about a recent health situation. Although, the child may have limited language and was unable or embarrassed to describe what happened to him, he was able to express it through a drawing. In this case, it was the teacher who made an immediate judgment call on the incident before consulting with the child and the parent. Some children do have a difficult time describing feelings about a situation, they may need some guidance and direction to help them sort through emotions that impact their personal situations.

INVOLVING PARENTS TO GET A PICTURE OF THE CHILD

When looking at delayed characteristics and determining autism, parents and professionals must seek to get a full picture of the child. The assessment should involve the parent and let parent express concerns about possible delays in the child's social interaction. This could include information about the child's affection with the parents and how the child interacts as part of the family. The parent can be a great asset to gain information about the child's communication patterns and how the child uses meaningful language and follows simple oral directions. The parent can also be useful in explaining the child's play patterns and how the child engages in pretend or imaginative play by him or herself and with other children.

If a parent thinks a child has autism the professional may ask 'why-do you think that?' Sometimes the answers are specific and based on a good understanding of autism characteristics. At other times, the parent is confused by things he or she has been told by professionals with limited knowledge about autism. The parents must keep exploring until they gain a better understanding of the characteristics of autism and other impairments or delays that impact their children.

Type of Educational Autism Assessment

Some school districts have early childhood clinics to help preschool students move into the public school settings. These clinics conduct educationally based autism assessments as well as other types of assessments for developmental delays, health issues and intellectual disabilities. Many times a school district will want at least two instruments to verify autism characteristics. Each state and district will vary in how they conduct these assessments. However, many clinics would use the following components as part of autism or developmental delay assessment:

Nursing/Health Assessment

The school nurse will provide several functions in his or her assessment of the child. The nurse will ask about the parent/family medical history, the birth/pregnancy history, and the developmental history (e.g. questions like 'when did he start walking?' or 'is the child toilet trained?'). The nurse may also conduct a vision screening, a hearing screening and check the child's dental status. The nurse may ask the child to complete a few tasks as he or she is also conducting a developmental delay screening. The nurse's contribution of medical knowledge really helps teams in determining the health impairments of the child. The nurse's I work with at a clinic are usually good spotters of things that other team members overlook. I have seen nurse's spot vision and hearing issues that changed the eligibility of the child.

Psycho-educational Assessment

The school psychologist will examine the child's cognitive abilities, school readiness skills, adaptive skills (e.g. communication, daily living, motor and socialization skills), examine autism characteristics, behavioral and emotional concerns and make testing observations (e.g. 'was the child cooperative, compliant or distracted, uncooperative or has a short attention span?'). The school psychologist can also have a role as a coordinator of all the team information. Many times the school psychologist completes the final multidisciplinary team report as other team members are sending him or her the child's assessment information. It is usually the school psychologist that presents the eligibility determination to the parent at the eligibility meeting.

Speech/Language Communication Assessment

The speech and language pathologist will examine several areas of the child. A communication and speech assessment will look at the child's language (e.g. both receptive and expressive language) and the child's speech sound system (phonological assessment). The speech and language assessment will also examine the voice and fluency of the child. The speech and language pathologist will also be observing how the child uses the pragmatics of language. He or she may also conduct and interview the parent with an autism instrument or checklist.

Occupational Therapy Assessment

The occupational therapist is involved in some assessments of children with autism and sensory issues. As part of the assessment, the occupational therapist will look at the child's eating and swallowing abilities. He or she will examine the child's fine motor and self help skills. If necessary, the occupational therapist will complete a sensory assessment. The occupational therapist will also make observations of the child (e.g. how the child activates toys, holds crayons, strength levels and motor coordination).

Physical Therapy Assessment

The physical therapist is an optional team member if

needed by the child. The physical therapist is helpful in examining the child's functional skills and looking at orthopedic information. The physical therapist can examine the child's sensory motor processes as well as mobility issues and how the child will adapt in the school environment. He or she can also provide assistance with needed equipment for the child in the school setting. If there are concerns on helping the child get transported to school and getting around the school safely then the physical therapist can help with these mobility issues.

SPECIAL EDUCATION TEACHER

The special education teacher is a valuable part of the multidisciplinary team assessment process. These special education teachers are often the first to meet the parent and conduct the intake with the parents as they arrive at the clinic. As part of the team the special education teacher often acquires valuable information from the intake that can quickly be shared with other team members on the child's concern or condition. The special education teacher is also involved in interviewing the parent to find out the skills of the child and the areas of difficulty. The special education teacher may assist with obtaining consent forms from doctors and the preschool the child is attending.

Sometimes the special education teacher will help the school psychologist by completing the school readiness assessment. This also helps the special education teacher who will be developing goals for the child as an individual educational plan is developed for the child. If necessary, the special education teacher can make a home observation if the team is unsure of some of the child's behaviors or skills. The special education teacher can also make a preschool or day care observation to see how the child interacts and performs in that setting. This really helps in determining the placement for a child in a special education or regular education program. After the assessment, the special education teacher works hard to develop the goals for the child's (e.g. if the child is eligible) individual education plan. The classroom special education teacher will then know what areas to write objectives

REGULAR EDUCATION TEACHER

The regular education teacher attends the eligibility meeting and is helpful in providing input when needed about the regular education expectations and classroom. The regular education teacher can often share experiences and observations from the school setting.

NOT A PERFECT WORLD

I wouldn't be being honest with you if I said the world of special education was a perfect world because it is not. I can talk with the special education professionals I have worked with for years and they will all tell you mistakes have been made in the process. There have been some kids identified with autism, a so called life long condition, that were exited out of the special education program by the second grade. There have been children with second language issues diagnosed with autism when there were major questions about how the second language issues impacted the child's language development. There have been children with major social risk factors and families with a strong history of mental illness given the autism eligibility when there were big questions about other behavioral issues that may better describe the child's actions and behaviors. In addition, some children with autism eligibilities would equally be a candidate for genetic testing because of unusual or atypical characteristics in their behavior, mannerisms and speech.

Professionals and parents must work together in the schools and educational environments to see how children progress with interventions and make changes when needed. Parents must be proactive for their children when educational needs are not being met and when issues need to be revisited at the schools. Professionals must be willing to accept when a placement really doesn't meet the child's needs. This is definitely a team approach all the way through school and it is important for the team to work together for the benefit of the child.

This book focused on determining if a child has characteristics of autism or developmental delays. I hope you see that it is not always an easy issue to resolve. Many children have developmental delays and children with autism characteristics also have developmental delays. We know that children with autism characteristics have delays and often present with uneven skill development. The question is whether the characteristics of autism are abundant in the child or whether there are just a few atypical, unusual or quirky types of behaviors that impact a child's development. On a final note, one must consider that children with autism exhibit delays, but not all children with delays exhibit an abundance of autism characteristics.

RECOMMENDED READING FOR AUTISM

Feinstein, A. (2010). *A history of autism: Conversations with the pioneers.* Hoboken, New Jersey: Wiley-Blackwell.

Hemenway, S. (2009). *The autism mom's survival guide.* Charleston, SC: BookSurge.

Robinson, R. (2011). *Autism solutions: How to create a healthy and meaningful life for your child.* Buffalo, NY: Harlequin.

Sears, R. (2010). *The autism book: What every parent needs to know about early detection, treatment, recovery and prevention.* Boston, MA: Little Brown and Company.

Vermeulen, P. (2012). *Autism as context blindness.* Overland Park, KS: AAPC Publishing.

INDEX

ABOUT THE AUTHOR

Susan Louise Peterson has worked professionally as a school psychologist, college faculty member and public school educator. When she started her educational career she had not even heard the word 'autism.' Over the years, Susan worked as a teacher of early childhood students and later became a school psychologist working in an early childhood diagnostic center where autism concerns were presented on a daily basis. Susan is the author of books in the areas of child behavior, education and research. Susan has lived in Las Vegas, NV for over 20 years. She spends her free time with her twin teenage daughters and husband.

CPSIA information can be obtained
at www.ICGtesting.com
Printed in the USA
LVOW12s1635090516

487376LV00001B/202/P